"THANK GOODNESS IT ISN'T A HATE CRIME!"

"THANK GOODNESS IT ISN'T A HATE CRIME!"

Cartoons by Wayne Stayskal

BakerBooks
A Division of Baker Book House Co
Grand Rapids, Michigan 49516

Published by Baker Books
a division of Baker Book House Company
P.O. Box 6287, Grand Rapids, MI 49516-6287

ISBN 0-8010-5060-X

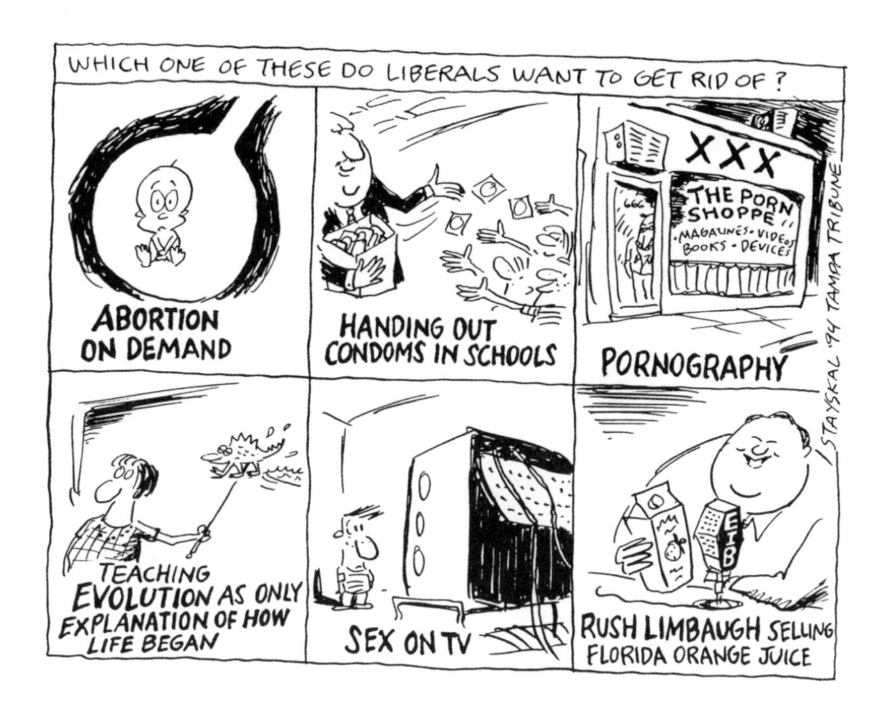
WHICH ONE OF THESE DO LIBERALS WANT TO GET RID OF ?
ABORTION ON DEMAND
HANDING OUT CONDOMS IN SCHOOLS
XXX
THE PORN SHOPPE
MAGAZINES • VIDEOS
BOOKS • DEVICES
PORNOGRAPHY
TEACHING EVOLUTION AS ONLY EXPLANATION OF HOW LIFE BEGAN
SEX ON TV
EIB
RUSH LIMBAUGH SELLING FLORIDA ORANGE JUICE
STAYSKAL '94 TAMPA TRIBUNE

WHAT DO THOSE MASKS REPRESENT ?
I THINK IT'S FOR PEOPLE WHO VOTED FOR CLINTON AND FOR THOSE WHO DIDN'T!
STAYSKAL '94 TAMPA TRIBUNE

FIRST CLASS STAMP TO GO UP TO 32¢
LOANS
STAMPS
U.S. POSTAL SERVICE
STAYSKAL 94 TAMPA TRIBUNE

STAYSKAL 94 TAMPA TRIBUNE
RELIGION IS CREEPING BACK INTO THE SCHOOLS... WE CAN TRY STOPPING IT, BUT I DON'T THINK WE HAVE A PRAYER!
ACLU
NOT THAT WE'D EVEN **WANT** ONE, OF COURSE!
ACLU

WOW! SENATOR DOLE GAVE US THE JOB OF PUSHING HIS IDEA TO MAKE ENGLISH THE OFFICIAL U.S. LANGUAGE. GREAT HUH?
RIGHT!
AHCOO
GESUNDHEIT!
STAYSKAL 95 TAMPA TRIBUNE

STAYSKAL 94 TAMPA TRIBUNE
...AND TODAY'S POLL SHOWS 62% DON'T BELIEVE YESTERDAY'S POLL!

TODAY'S GUEST REPRESENTS THE TOBACCO INDUSTRY!
I WOULD JUST LIKE TO...
...SAY THAT...
...NICOTINE...
...AHHHH...
...ISN'T ADDICTIVE!
STAYSKAL '94 TAMPA TRIBUNE

CLINTON SIGNS BILL TO USE FEDERAL MONEY TO IMPROVE LEARNING IN PUBLIC SCHOOLS... SOME WORRY THERE'LL BE STRINGS ATTACHED.
SEE BILLY. SEE BILLY RUN. RUN, BILLY, RUN. SEE HILLARY. SEE HILLARY RUN. RUN, HILLARY, RUN. SEE SOCKS...
STAYSKAL '94 TAMPA TRIBUNE

CLINTON PUSHING HARD TO SELL HEALTH PROGRAM. HIS STRATEGY SAYS AIDE, IS "REPETITION, REPETITION, REPETITION."
YOU NEED MY PLAN... YOU NEED MY PLAN... YOU NEED MY PLAN..
THERE'S GOT TO BE A BETTER WAY... THERE'S GOT TO BE A BETTER WAY... THERE'S GOT TO BE A BETTER WAY...
STAYSKAL 94 TAMPA TRIBUNE

THE WORLD'S PRESS CONDUCTS A GLOBAL SEARCH
CAFFE' PO
COME ON, ANTON! IF IT'S NOT MICHAEL JACKSON, FORGET IT!
STAYSKAL 93 TAMPA TRIBUNE

"I'M SORRY BUT YOU CAN HAVE BRONCHITIS ONLY ON EVEN MONDAYS... WOULD YOU LIKE TO SWITCH TO KIDNEY STONES OR PNEUMONIA?"

"I'M GETTIN' AN EARLY RELEASE... SAVE MY PLACE IN LINE, WILL YA?"

ANOTHER MEMBER OF CONGRESS SAYS HE WON'T RUN FOR RE-ELECTION!
THAT'S TERRIBLE! IF THIS KEEPS UP THERE WON'T BE ANYBODY LEFT TO THROW OUT!
STAYSKAL 94 TAMPA TRIBUNE

WHAT HAPPENED!? I JUST GAVE YOU A PERM 2 DAYS AGO!
I JUST READ THE DETAILS OF CLINTON'S HEALTH CARE PLAN!
STAYSKAL 94 TAMPA TRIBUNE

I PROMISED CHANGE AND I WILL FULFILL THAT PROMISE. FIRST, I WILL CHANGE MY PROMISE TO GIVE THE MIDDLE CLASS A TAX CUT AND TO CHOP THE DEFICIT IN HALF. NEXT...
INAUGURATION
STAYSKAL 93 TAMPA TRIBUNE

TRANS FATTY ACIDS IN MARGARINE WORSE THAN SATURATED FAT, SAY RESEARCHERS
SPREADS
MARGARINE SUBSTITUTE
CHEESE
BUTTER
FLAKES
MILK
STAYSKAL 94 TAMPA TRIBUNE

THERE ISN'T A PARENTAL 'SMUT FILTER' I CAN'T OVERRIDE!
ON-LINE AMERICA
STAYSKAL '95 TAMPA TRIBUNE

FELKAMPS CAMPAIGN BUTTONS, CO.
WE CAN MAKE A KILLING WHETHER SHE RUNS OR NOT!
HILLARY FOR PRESIDENT
HILLARY WAS PRESIDENT
STAYSKAL '94 TAMPA TRIBUNE

"I'VE GOT TO ADMIT THE NEW LABELING SYSTEM IS GREAT!"

SOCIALIZED HEALTH CARE ADMIN.
WAIT
I KNOW YOU NEED THE OPERATION... BUT DON'T YOU REALIZE YOU'RE NEARLY 4 YEARS OVER LIFE EXPECTANCY AS IT IS?!
TREATMENT RATIONING
STAYSKAL 94 TAMPA TRIBUNE

EEOC PUSHES FOR RELIGION TO BE INCLUDED IN WORKPLACE HARRASSMENT GUIDELINES
I HEARD SOMEBODY MENTION GOD OUT HERE AND I WANT IT STOPPED... UNLESS, OF COURSE, YOU WERE JUST SWEARING!
STAYSKAL 94 TAMPA TRIBUNE

LEROY, GO TO THE BLACKBOARD AND WRITE A 3-LETTER WORD THAT BEGINS WITH 'G'... IT'S SOMETHING WE DON'T ALLOW IN SCHOOL!
God
GUN-TOTING JUVENILES
NAFTA
STAYSKAL '93 TAMPA TRIBUNE

PSSSST... FILTHY PICTURES?
SURE... IS $75,000 OKAY?
NAT'L ENDOWMENT FOR THE ARTS
STAYSKAL '94 TAMPA TRIBUNE

SPELLING BEE
HIDDEN TAX
E-M-P-L-O-Y-E-R H-E-A-L-T-H M-A-N-D-A-T-E-S
BILLY CLINTON
STAYSKAL '94 TAMPA TRIBUNE

BUT I DIDN'T SAY ANYTHING ABOUT THE RELIGIOUS RIGHT. I SAID JESUS ATE WITH THE PUBLICANS... NOT REPUBLICANS!
STAYSKAL '94 TAMPA TRIBUNE

ENDANGERED SPECIES
OFF THE LIST
STILL ON THE LIST*
*CLINTON-STYLE HEALTH CARE PLANS STILL INCLUDE ABORTION
STAYSKAL 94 TAMPA TRIBUNE

WHO ASKED YOU TO WORK OVERTIME? WHAT TIME DID YOU START? WHAT TIME DID YOU FINISH? WHAT TIME DID YOU LEAVE? DID ANYONE SEE YOU LEAVE? WHAT ROUTE DID YOU TAKE HOME? HOW MANY...
YOU'VE BEEN WATCHING THE O.J. SIMPSON HEARINGS, HAVEN'T YOU?
STAYSKAL 94 TAMPA TRIBUNE

HEALTH CARE AS IT IS
I THINK I'D LIKE A SECOND OPINION!
THAT'LL BE FINE... I UNDERSTAND YOUR CONCERN!
DOCTOR
SOCIALIZED HEALTH CARE
I THINK I'D LIKE A SECOND OPINION!
A SECOND OPINION!!? HEY, SLADE... WANNA HEAR A GOOD ONE?!!
MEDICAL ADMINISTRATOR
STAYSKAL '94 TAMPA TRIBUNE

Dear Folks,
Learning to be President up here at the U of Washington, D.C. is really fun. Send money.
love, Bill
P.S. Hillary says 'hi'.
U.S. MAIL
STAYSKAL '93 TAMPA TRIBUNE

"IS THERE AN HMO PROVIDER IN THE HOUSE?"

" MY HAT'S OFF TO YOU, JOHNSON... EVERYBODY ELSE COMES IN ASKING FOR A RAISE! "

PORT-AU-PRINCE
STAYSKAL '94 TAMPA TRIBUNE

CAN'T YOU TAKE A BREAK, HENRY? THE PRESIDENT'S ON TV TELLING US HOW BAD THINGS ARE IN HAITI!

CLINTON'S BIG GOVERNMENT HEALTH-CARE PLANS ARE DEAD FOR THIS YEAR
BREATHE A SIGH OF RELIEF!
STAYSKAL 94 TAMPA TRIBUNE

STAYSKAL 93 TAMPA TRIBUNE
PRAYING? ER... NO, MA'AM. THEY WERE SO WOBBLY FROM THEIR LONG VOYAGE THEY JUST FELL TO THEIR KNEES ON THE BEACH!

"REMEMBER WHEN DEMOCRATIC INCUMBENTS USED TO ASK FOR VOTES BY WALKING THROUGH AND SHAKING HANDS?"

CLINTON'S EXPLANATION FOR HIS LOW RATINGS
IF PEOPLE ONLY UNDERSTOOD WHAT I'VE BEEN PROPOSING, THEY WOULD HAVE BEEN FOR IT.
DID HE JUST CALL US NITWITS?
SURE DID... BUT I DON'T THINK HE THOUGHT ANYBODY WOULD UNDERSTAND!
STAYSKAL 94 TAMPA TRIBUNE

FULTON COUNTY, GEORGIA, REQUIRES WARNING LABEL ON NEWLY PURCHASED GUNS
EVIDENTLY THAT GUY JUST DOESN'T CARE HOW DANGEROUS THAT GUN CAN BE TO HIMSELF AND HIS FAMILY
STAYSKAL 94 TAMPA TRIBUNE

"I SEE A LOT OF THIS WHEN THE ELECTION RACES HEAT UP... THEY'RE SOUND BITES!"

I SURVIVED MANY ATTEMPTS TO END ABORTION
I DIDN'T
STAYSKAL 95 TAMPA TRIBUNE

NEWS: BETTER EDUCATED AMERICANS ARE ALSO MUCH HEALTHIER
TAKE YOUR MEDICINE EVERY MORNING AND GO BACK TO COLLEGE FOR A MASTER'S DEGREE!
DOCTOR
STAYSKAL 95 TAMPA TRIBUNE

"NO, WE DON'T HAVE A HANDGUN IN THE HOUSE FOR PROTECTION!"

"HEY, GUESS WHAT?.. I GET MY 10-YEAR PIN NEXT MONTH!"

"I SUPPOSE IF THE REPUBLICANS HAVE THEIR WAY WE'LL REALLY HAVE TO WORK FOR FOOD SOMEDAY!"

WE DROPPED OUR AFFIRMATIVE ACTION HIRING POLICY FOR ONE THAT'S FAIRER TO EVERYBODY!
PERSONNEL DEPT.
LONG MATCHSTICK WINS!
STAYSKAL '95 TAMPA TRIBUNE

POSTAL SERVICE
STAMPS
SERVICE
GOING UP!
GOING DOWN!
STAYSKAL '14 TAMPA TRIBUNE

"I'D LIKE A RAISE BECAUSE WHAT I MAKE NOW ISN'T ALLOWING ME TO TAKE PART IN THE RISE OF CONSUMER CONFIDENCE!"

"I WISH THEY'D TEACH CREATIONISM TOO... I NEVER DID BELIEVE IN THE LITERAL INTERPRETATION OF DARWIN!"

SOME DOCTORS PUSH FOR PATENTING MEDICAL PROCEDURES
YOU SAY HE GOT RICH FROM LICENSING A MEDICAL PROCEDURE? WHICH ONE IS IT?
'TAKE TWO ASPIRIN AND CALL ME IN THE MORNING'!
NURSES
STAYSKAL 95 TAMPA TRIBUNE

ELDERS SAYS SHE BELIEVES SHE RAISED AWARENESS OF SOCIAL ISSUES!
ALL SHE EVER RAISED WERE EYEBROWS!
FIRED SURGEON GENERAL DEFENDS SELF
STAYSKAL 94 TAMPA TRIBUNE

THAT WAS THE PRESIDENT'S ADDRESS TO THE NATION
WELL, AT LEAST WE KNOW WHERE HE STANDS FOR THE MOMENT!
STAYSKAL 94 TAMPA TRIBUNE

GOP
STAYSKAL 94 TAMPA TRIBUNE

I TOLD YOU THE REPUBLICANS WOULDN'T KNOW HOW TO RUN THINGS!
YOU'RE RIGHT... THERE HASN'T BEEN A MOTION TO RAISE OUR SALARY YET!
DEMOCRATIC HOUSE OFFICES
STAYSKAL 95 TAMPA TRIBUNE

GUESS IT'S TRUE ... MOMS ARE IGNORING THE EXPERTS!
YEAH... OURS RIPPED OUT THE CHAPTER ON WHY SPANKING KIDS IS BAD FROM THIS ONE, TOO!
CHILD REARING DR.
STAYSKAL 95 TAMPA TRIBUNE

MRS CLINTON SAYS HER HEALTH CARE PLAN FAILED BECAUSE SHE WAS 'NAÏVE AND DUMB' ABOUT NATIONAL POLITICS!
YOU BELIEVE THAT?
DO I LOOK NAÏVE AND DUMB!?
STAYSKAL 95 TAMPA TRIBUNE

DON'T FORGET... YOU HAVE AN AFTER-NOON NEWS CONFERENCE TO CLAIM YOU ALREADY THOUGHT OF WHATEVER NEW IDEAS THE GOP COMES UP WITH THIS MORNING!
REP. GEPHARDT
DEMOCRAT
STAYSKAL 95 TAMPA TRIBUNE

HIGH BLOOD PRESSURE ON THE INCREASE
YOU HAVE A CHOICE OF TREATMENT. TAKE THESE PILLS OR STOP WATCHING NETWORK NEWS!
STAYSKAL '95 TAMPA TRIBUNE

THE FUGITIVE
(THE MOVIE)
HE WENT THIS WAY!
AFTER HIM!
THE FUGITIVE
(REAL LIFE)
THERE HE GOES, BILL!
DON'T LET HIM GET AWAY, AL!!
TAXPAYER
STAYSKAL '93 TAMPA TRIBUNE

TWO TYPES OF LITTLE GREEN PEOPLE
THOSE FROM OUTER SPACE
HZBJ LKY!
NUFK LZAVD TVLYR!
THOSE IN CONGRESS
DEMOCRATS
NEWT'S BOOK SHOULDN'T BE WORTH MORE THAN 2 CENTS!
I'D NEVER READ IT!
I'M GLAD THEY DIDN'T ASK ME!
I'D HAVE LAUGHED IN THEIR FACE!
I HIRED AN AGENT TO TELL PUBLISHERS I'M NOT INTERESTED
I'D NEVER AGREE TO DO A BOOK
STAYSKAL '95 TAMPA TRIBUNE

ABORTION CLINIC
LIFE BEGINS AT BIRTH!
YOU MEAN THE THING IN ME ISN'T ALIVE?
THAT'S RIGHT!
THEN WHY DO I NEED AN ABORTION?
COUNSELING SERVICE
STAYSKAL '95 TAMPA TRIBUNE

THE SENATE IS AGAIN GOING TO TRY TO CLEAN SMUT FROM TV!
THAT'S GOOD... EXCEPT JUNIOR HASN'T WATCHED TV SINCE HE WENT ON-LINE WITH HIS COMPUTER!
PORN PHOTOS
SEX CLUBS
STAYSKAL 95 TAMPA TRIBUNE

SOME REBEL AGAINST HEALTH MESSAGE.. PICK UP OLD HABIT
SAM DIED?! GEE, AND HE JUST STARTED SMOKING AGAIN... WAS IT CANCER?
NO... PNEUMONIA!
NO SMOKING IN BUILDING
STAYSKAL 93 TAMPA TRIBUNE

STAYSKAL 95 TAMPA TRIBUNE
WE'RE GOING TO BREAK AWAY FROM OUR COVERAGE OF THE SIMPSON TRIAL FOR AN UPDATE ON THE NEWS!
THE O.J. SIMPSON TRIAL MOVED ALONG TODAY WITH THE DEFENSE TEAM TRYING TO OFFSET THE TESTIMONY OF PROSECUTION WITNESSES!
AND NOW WE RETURN YOU TO THE SIMPSON TRIAL!

...AND REPRESENTING THE RELIGIOUS RIGHT IS...
ALL THEY WANNA DO IS RAM THEIR MORALITY DOWN OUR THROATS!
HOW COME YOU NEVER SAY ANYTHING WHEN SOMEBODY DOES THE SAME WITH IMMORALITY?
STAYSKAL 95 TAMPA TRIBUNE

ACLU
THEY CAUGHT SOME STUDENTS DOING IT AGAIN!
PRAYING?
NO... CARRYING GUNS TO CLASS!
OH! WERE ANY OF THEIR RIGHTS VIOLATED?
STAYSKAL 95 TAMPA TRIBUNE

CLINTON THREATENS TO VETO GOP BILL LETTING COMMUNITIES SPEND ANTI-CRIME MONEY AS THEY SEE FIT
BURGLARY IN PROGRESS
TOO BAD CLINTON MADE US HIRE MORE POLICEMEN WITH HIS ANTI-CRIME MONEY. WE REALLY NEEDED ANOTHER SQUAD CAR!
STAYSKAL 95 TAMPA TRIBUNE

GOVERNMENT SPENDING HAS GOT TO BE CUT!
YOU'RE RIGHT!
LET'S START WITH WELFARE!
PEOPLE WILL STARVE. HOW ABOUT THE MILITARY?
THAT'LL BLOW OUR DEFENSE. CUT INFRASTRUCTURE!
BRIDGES AND ROADS WILL CRUMBLE!
SOCIAL SECURITY? EDUCATION?
THEN HOW CAN WE KEEP FROM GOING BROKE?
PERISH THE THOUGHT!
STAYSKAL 95 TAMPA TRIBUNE

STAYSKAL 95 TAMPA TRIBUNE
DID YOU SAY YOU SAW THE FIRST ROBIN OF SPRING?
NO... THE FIRST POLLSTER OF '96!
POLL
THE CAMPAIGN FOR THE GOP PRESIDENTIAL NOMINATION HAS OFFICIALLY BEGUN...

GINGRICH SAYS GOVERNMENT SHOULDN'T FUND THE NATIONAL ENDOWMENT FOR THE ARTS!
EVER HEAR ANYTHING SO OBSCENE?
NOT SINCE YOU FIRST DESCRIBED THE IDEA FOR THAT PAINTING YOU'RE WORKING ON!
STAYSKAL 95 TAMPA TRIBUNE

GOP'S CONTRACT WITH AMERICA
I BELIEVE THIS IS SOME OF YOUR HARD EARNED MONEY!
DEM'S CONTACT WITH AMERICA
OOOOPS... SORRY! PARDON ME!
STAYSKAL 95 TAMPA TRIBUNE

FLORIDA FILES $1.4 BILLION SUIT AGAINST THE TOBACCO INDUSTRY
YOUR HONOR, I'D LIKE TO MOVE THAT THE WITNESS'S LAST COMMENT, 'HACK, COUGH, COUGH, COUGH, WHEEZE, HACK, COUGH,' BE STRICKEN FROM THE RECORD!
TOBACCO
FLORIDA
STAYSKAL 95 TAMPA TRIBUNE

NEWS: NEARLY 3 IN 4 AMERICANS ARE OVERWEIGHT
HOW CAN I TELL IF I'M OVERWEIGHT WHEN THE SCALE KEEPS BREAKING?
STAYSKAL 95 TAMPA TRIBUNE

FEDERALLY RUN SCHOOL-LUNCH PROGRAM
FEDERAL ADMINISTRATORS
HERE YOU ARE, KIDS!
STATE RUN SCHOOL-LUNCH PROGRAM... FEDERALLY FUNDED THROUGH BLOCK GRANTS
HERE YOU ARE, KIDS!
STAYSKAL 95 TAMPA TRIBUNE

DEMOCRATS BLOCK BALANCED-BUDGET AMENDMENT
I DON'T KNOW WHAT LIBERALS LIKE BEST... SPENDING MORE...
...OR STOPPING CONSERVATIVES FROM SPENDING LESS!
STAYSKAL 95 TAMPA TRIBUNE

MORE STATES SEEK TO LET CITIZENS CARRY CONCEALED WEAPONS

VOTERS' CONTRACT WITH AMERICA
IN 1996 WE WILL THROW OUT MORE LIBERALS!
STAYSKAL '95 TAMPA TRIBUNE

DEM CLOAKROOM
WHO'LL-CHARGE-GINGRICH WITH-SOMETHING-OR-OTHER-NEXT SCHEDULE
STAYSKAL '95 TAMPATRIBUNE

"THE GOOD NEWS IS NONE OF THE STUFF THEY MENTION IS FATTENING!"

FIRST LADY LASHES OUT AT CONSERVATIVE TALK SHOW HOSTS
THEY'RE TOLD WHAT TO SAY AND DO A DISSERVICE TO AMERICA!
WELCOME TO THE SHOW, FOLKS! HEY, GUESS WHAT? THE WHITE HOUSE FLIP-FLOPPED AGAIN... THIS TIME ON 'V-J DAY'!..
STAYSKAL '95 TAMPA TRIBUNE

AND NOW TONIGHT'S FEATURE, 'HONEY, I SHRUNK THE GOVERNMENT', STARRING NEWT GINGRICH...
STAYSKAL '95 TAMPA TRIBUNE

MORE AND MORE NEWSPAPERS ARE GOING ON-LINE WITH ELECTRONIC EDITIONS
WHEW... OH, FOR THE GOOD OLD DAYS!
CUBS
STAYSKAL 95 TAMPA TRIBUNE

MEMBERS OF THE HOUSE WHO VOTED AGAINST TERM LIMITS
'96 RE-ELECTION HOPES
STAYSKAL 95 TAMPA TRIBUNE

ISN'T THAT ONE OF THOSE REPLACEMENT PLAYERS AT THE PLATE?
ARE YOU KIDDING?! DO YOU THINK THEY'D PAY A REPLACEMENT PLAYER $12 MILLION TO BAT .192?
STAYSKAL '95 TAMPA TRIBUNE

ASTRONOMERS STUDY MARS AFTER DISCOVERY OF ANCIENT EXPLOSION THAT HURTLED ROCKS TO EARTH.
HOLY COW! SPECTROSCOPE TESTS ON THOSE RED SPOTS ON MARS SHOW THEY'RE O.J.'s BLOOD!
STAYSKAL '95 TAMPA TRIBUNE

AND ON THE 101ST DAY THEY RESTED.
BILL
HOUSE REPUBLICANS
STAYSKAL '95 TAMPA TRIBUNE

COURT
I HOPE NOTHING HAPPENS IN COURT WHILE I'M OUT... I JUST HAD TO TAKE A QUICK SMOKE!
WHAT ARE YOU COVERING?
PRESS
THOSE CHARGES AGAINST THE TOBACCO COMPANIES THAT CIGARETTES ARE ADDICTIVE!
PRESS
STAYSKAL '95 TAMPA TRIBUNE

DEMOCRATIC CLOAKROOM
WELL, IF YOU DON'T LIE LIKE THE REST OF US ABOUT THE GOP STARVING SCHOOL KIDS, YOU'LL STICK OUT LIKE A SORE THUMB AROUND HERE!
STAYSKAL '95 TAMPA TRIBUNE

...AND YOU CAN OWN THIS SET OF 199 VIDEOTAPES OF THE O.J. TRIAL FOR JUST $1,999.95. RELIVE EVERY MOMENT. CALL NOW. 1-800-024-6
STAYSKAL '95 TAMPA TRIBUNE

CLINTON SAYS HE'LL LEAD FROM NOW ON
HOLD IT! IT'S TIME FOR ME TO TAKE...
HOUSE GOP
...OVER!
STAYSKAL 95 TAMPA TRIBUNE

WHAT ARE THEY YELLIN' ABOUT? DON'T WE ALREADY FLATTEN THEM ENOUGH EACH YEAR?
I.R.S.
VOTERS WANT FLAT TAX
STAYSKAL 95 TAMPA TRIBUNE

" SURE IS NIPPY TODAY... LOOKS LIKE WE'RE IN FOR A LONG, COLD WINTER ! "

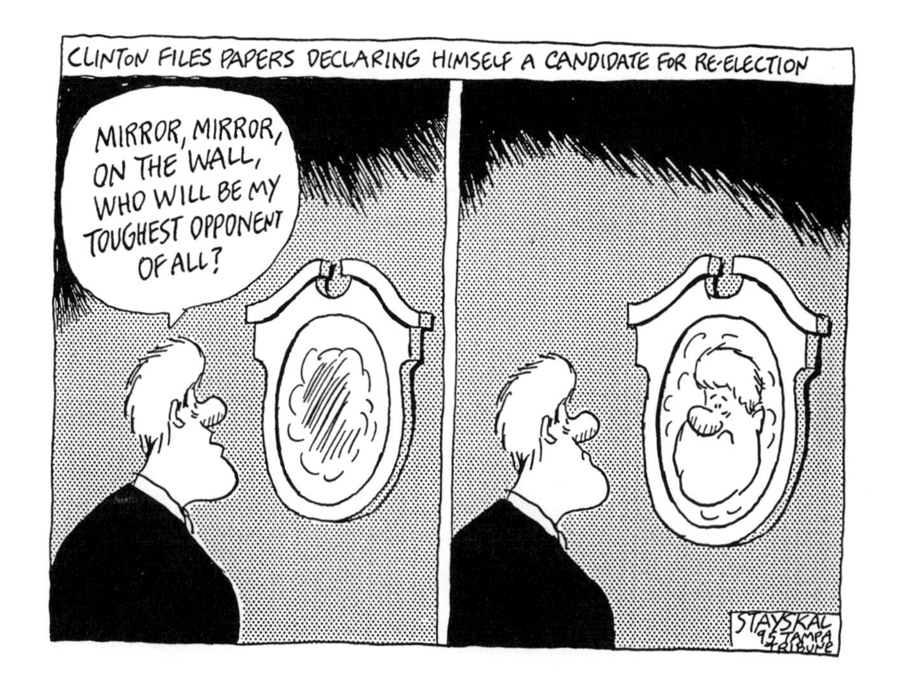

"SEE HOW DANGEROUS IT IS TO ALLOW PEOPLE TO HAVE EASY ACCESS TO GUNS?"

RESEARCHERS SAY QUALITY OF SERVICE ON AIRLINES DECLINED FOR 4TH YEAR IN A ROW
TICKETS
WHAT SECTION WOULD YOU LIKE...LOST LUGGAGE OR OVERBOOKED?
DEPARTURES
STAYSKAL '95 TAMPA TRIBUNE

THE PROSECUTION'S DNA EVIDENCE WAS REFUTED BY THE DEFENSE TODAY. THEY CLAIM THE POL
THERMOMETER
BAROMETER
HUMIDITY
O.J. TRIAL
STAYSKAL '95 TAMPA TRIBUNE

MOM SAYS WE'RE GOIN' TO DR FOSTER'S... PROBABLY WANTS TO SIGN US UP FOR HIS 'I HAVE A FUTURE' PROGRAM!
DR FOSTER ABORTIONIST
STAYSKAL 95 TAMPA TRIBUNE

GOVERNMENT BEGINS MOVING NASA TOWARD PRIVATE MANAGEMENT
WE'VE GOT TWO INTERESTED PARTIES. THE JOINT EFFORT OF ROCKWELL CORP AND LOCKHEED-MARTIN, AND THE TEAM OF TOM HANKS AND UNIVERSAL PICTURES!
NASA
APOLLO 13
STAYSKAL 95 TAMPA TRIBUNE

"LAST SPRING YOU ROBBED ME AND GOT 3 YEARS. LAST MONTH YOU NAILED ME AGAIN AND GOT 5 TO 10... HAVEN'T YOU LEARNED YOUR LESSON YET?"

IT'S FROM DR KEVORKIAN?
HE SAYS IF HE'S EVER SENT TO PRISON COULD HE HAVE A JOB ON DEATH ROW?
WARDEN
STAYSKAL 95 TAMPA TRIBUNE

SENATORS URGE 'REPORT CARD' TO ALERT PARENTS TO THE MOST VIOLENT TV PROGRAMS
I WISH OUR 'REPORT CARD' WOULD COME SO WE COULD TELL IF THIS IS ONE OF THOSE 'MOST VIOLENT' TV SHOWS!
STAYSKAL 95 TAMPA TRIBUNE

HE'S MADE MILLIONS IN THE LAST FEW MONTHS? HOW?
HE INVENTED THE LINE 'CRUEL AND HEARTLESS REPUBLICANS' AND SOLD IT TO THE DEMOCRATS!
STAYSKAL 95 TAMPA TRIBUNE

THE NEWS: PENTAGON MISPLACES BILLIONS
WOULD YOU BELIEVE IT, MARTHA... I DIDN'T MISPLACE A DARNED THING TODAY!
I DON'T KNOW WHO HE IS... HE JUST WALKED IN, SAT DOWN AND LOOSENED HIS TIE!
GEN. ZILTCH
STAYSKAL 95 TAMPA TRIBUNE

WHAT!? YOU HEARD MORE WILL JUMP TO THE REPUBLICANS? CONGRESSMEN OR SENATORS?
WORSE!! VOTERS!
DEMOCRATS
DEM REP. SWITCHES TO GOP
STAYSKAL 95 TAMPA TRIBUNE

TARIFFS COULD DOUBLE PRICES OF SOME JAPANESE AUTOS
TRYING TO DECIDE BETWEEN THE XL300 OR THE VM300?
NO... BETWEEN A CAR OR A HOUSE!
XL300
STAYSKAL 95 TAMPA TRIBUNE

CONGRESSMEN ASK SPORTS ILLUSTRATED TO DROP TOBACCO ADS
THEY SHOULD ASK THEM TO DROP A WHOLE LOT MORE THAN THAT!
HEY, HAS ANYBODY SEEN MY SWIMSUIT ISSUE?
STAYSKAL 95 TAMPA

GOD, WHY HAVEN'T YOU SENT US PEOPLE WITH CURES FOR CANCER AND AIDS, AND ANSWERS TO WORLD HUNGER AND ALL OUR SOCIAL PROBLEMS?
I DID!
BUT... BUT... WHERE ARE THEY?!
YOU ABORTED THEM!
STAYSKAL 93 TAMPA TRIBUNE

VIRGINIA TO LIMIT HANDGUN PURCHASES TO ONE PER MONTH PER CUSTOMER

"GOOD-BY... WE REALLY ENJOYED HAVING YOU... HOPE YOU'LL LIKE IT IN WASHINGTON. COME BACK AND SEE US SOMETIME, OKAY?"

NEWS: THE LEADING CAUSE OF ON-THE-JOB DEATHS IN NEW YORK IS HOMICIDE.

WOW! LOOK AT ALL THOSE PEOPLE ADDICTED TO STANDING IN THE RAIN!
PHILIP MORRIS CIGARETTE COMPANY
THIS IS A SMOKE FREE BUILDING
THANK YOU FOR NOT SMOKING
STAYSKAL 93 TAMPA TRIBUNE

LOOK ★!!%# &★@!, WE NEED MORE Ç!!★#% FAMILY MOVIES, ★★!#% IT!
HOW ABOUT ★✱!!Ç★ CATS AND DOGS AND SOME !!#★?%@ KIDS. NO ★!@#!! SWEARING OR #Ç!%#★★✱!! SEX. JUST !!#?!★@ MORAL STUFF!
SOUNDS GOOD, ★!!✱?# IT. THE ✱#!!★★ FANS WILL EAT THE ★?@!!#★✱ UP. IT'LL BE GOOD DOING SOMETHING THATS ★!!@# UPLIFTING FOR A !#★@✱ CHANGE!
HOLLYWOOD
FAMILY FILMS MAKE MONEY
GOMORRAH STUDIOS
STAYSKAL 93 TAMPA TRIBUNE

"IT WAS MADE AT THE OLD TRIDENT MISSILE PLANT!"

"IT'S GOT SOMETHING TO DO WITH HEALTH CARE REFORM!"

WHY DON'T YOU THINK YOUR STRESS IS COMING FROM THE JOB YOU'RE DOING?
BECAUSE IT'S COMING FROM THE JOB BILL CLINTON IS DOING!
STAYSKAL 93 TAMPA TRIBUNE

EAT
MUGGER CROSSING
NEXT 5 BLOCKS
STAYSKAL 93 TAMPA TRIBUNE

"BACK FROM THE IRS ALREADY? HOW DID IT GO?"

THE INCREDIBLE SHRINKING MAN

AFTER 100 DAYS PRESIDENT CLINTON SAYS HE'S STILL COMMITTED TO CHANGE!
WELL, I BELIEVE HIM. HE'S ALREADY CHANGED 'TAX-AND-SPEND' TO 'SPEND-AND-TAX'!
STAYSKAL 93 TAMPA TRIBUNE

STAYSKAL 93 TAMPA TRIBUNE
"I EXPECTED THE 25 YEARS... BUT NO EARLY RELEASE UNTIL A WEEK FROM THURSDAY WAS A LITTLE STIFF, I THOUGHT!"

CLINTON'S FIRST 100 DAYS...
100 DAYS?!! I COULD HAVE SWORN IT WAS 100 YEARS!
STAYSKAL 93 TAMPA TRIBUNE

STAYSKAL 93 TAMPA TRIBUNE
I HEAR THEY REVOKED YOUR LICENSE TO PRACTICE MEDICINE?!
YES... BUT DON'T WORRY. THIS IS A LOT MORE FUN!
KEVORKIAN BUNGEE JUMP

HILLARY SAYS THE BEST WAY TO PAY FOR HER BILLION-DOLLAR HEALTH-CARE PLAN IS THROUGH A PAYROLL DEDUCTION.
I WANT A SECOND OPINION!
STAYSKAL '93 TAMPA TRIBUNE

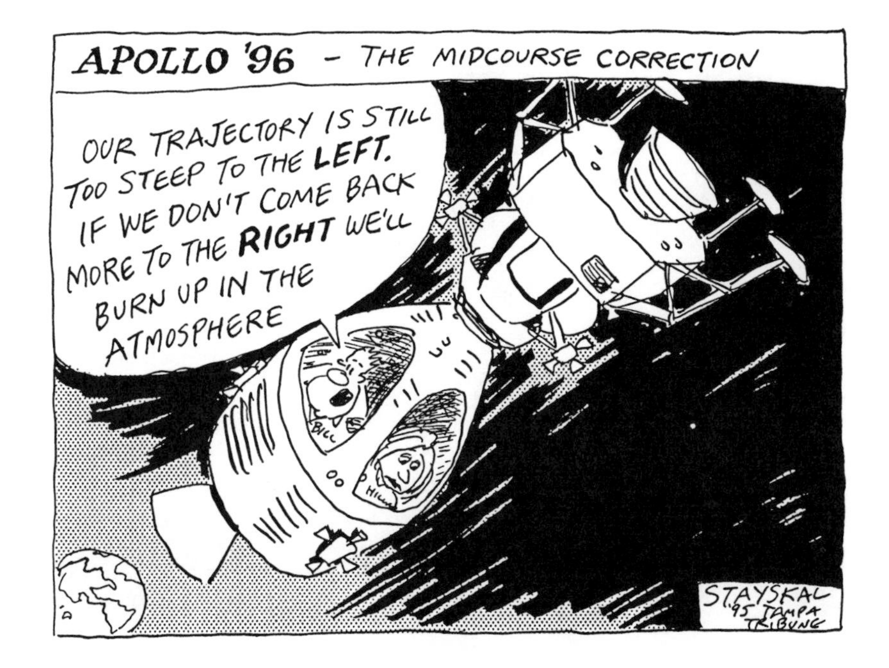
APOLLO '96 - THE MIDCOURSE CORRECTION
OUR TRAJECTORY IS STILL TOO STEEP TO THE LEFT. IF WE DON'T COME BACK MORE TO THE RIGHT WE'LL BURN UP IN THE ATMOSPHERE
BILL
HILL
STAYSKAL '95 TAMPA TRIBUNE

JANUARY, 1997
HOLY ELECTION RESULTS, BATMAN. I FIGURED PEOPLE WOULD KNOW WE WERE KIDDING WHEN WE TOSSED OUR HATS IN THE RING AS INDEPENDENT CANDIDATES!
THE PRESIDENT OF THE UNITED STATES
SEAL OF THE PRESIDENT OF THE UNITED STATES
STAYSKAL 95 TAMPA TRIBUNE

BECAUSE OF THEIR INVESTMENTS IN HEALTH STOCKS, THE CLINTONS WILL PUT THEIR ASSETS INTO A BLIND TRUST!
BLIND TRUST?! ISN'T THAT THE SAME THING WE DID WHEN WE VOTED FOR HIM?
STAYSKAL 93 TAMPA TRIBUNE

STAYSKAL
93 TAMPA
TRIBUNE
MIDDLE CLASS
WILL WORK TO PAY TAXES

STAYSKAL
93 TAMPA
TRIBUNE
ARE YOU FOR OR AGAINST GUN CONTROL?
I'M FOR IT!
POLL
WELCOME
AND LOOK... I'M GETTING PRETTY GOOD AT IT, TOO!
POLL
WELCOME

POSTAL SERVICE BANS SMOKING IN ALL THEIR BUILDINGS AND OFFICES

"CLINTON WAS RIGHT... MORE TAXES AND SPENDING HAS CREATED WORK. I'VE NEVER BEEN SO BUSY!"

"LOOKS LIKE A CASE OF 'PARENTAL DISCRETION'!"

"THANK GOODNESS IT ISN'T A HATE CRIME!"

"PERSONALLY, I LIKE TV VIOLENCE... IT KEEPS VIEWERS FROM YELLING ABOUT ALL THE SEX!"

...LARGE STOCKPILES OF ANTHRAX AND VARIOUS BOTULIN THAT CAUSE BOTULISM!
IF THE NEWS OF IRAQ HAVING STORES OF BIOLOGICAL WEAPONS MAKES YOU NERVOUS, WHY WATCH?
STAYSKAL 95 TAMPA TRIBUNE

THE PRESIDENT SURVEYING ANOTHER DISASTER AREA
STAYSKAL 93 TAMPA TRIBUNE
WHY IS IT SO RED?
IT'S INK, SIR!

DON'T ASK, DON'T TELL!
IS HE ANSWERING QUESTIONS ABOUT GAYS IN THE MILITARY AGAIN?
NO... ABOUT HOW MUCH HIS TAX PACKAGE IS REALLY GOING TO COST!
STAYSKAL 93 TAMPA TRIBUNE

NO, WE DON'T KEEP A GUN IN THE HOUSE FOR PROTECTION!
THANK YOU, MADAM!
POLL
BUT WE DO KEEP THE YARD MINED!
STAYSKAL 93 TAMPA TRIBUNE

ARE YOU FOR TERM LIMITS?
ABSOLUTELY... WHEN THEY CATCH US WITH OUR HANDS IN THE TILL, WE SHOULDN'T GET ANY MORE THAN 18 MONTHS!
STAYSKAL 93 TAMPA TRIBUNE

I GOT THE IDEA FROM TELEVISION!
I GOT THE IDEA FROM THE NEWS!
TV DIRECTOR
STAYSKAL 93 TAMPA TRIBUNE

WHAT AILS DEMOCRATIC PARTY IS LACK OF CONSISTENT MESSAGE, EXPERTS SAY
WELL, I SAY THE EXPERTS ARE WRONG!
YEAH! THEY FORGOT TAX AND SPEND, TAX AND SPEND. WHAT'S MORE CONSISTENT THAN THAT?
DEMOCRATIC PA
STAYSKAL '95 TAMPA TRIBUNE

NEWS ITEM: LOCAL PHONE COMPANIES FREE TO ENTER CABLE TV BUSINESS
THE PHONE PEOPLE HAVE THEIR LINES CROSSED AGAIN... THIS IS SUPPOSED TO BE ESPN, NOT MRS. WIGGONS NEXT DOOR!
STAYSKAL '93 TAMPA TRIBUNE

"THESE NEW SHOWS INSULT MY INTELLIGENCE... AND TO MAKE IT WORSE, I'LL HAVE TO WATCH THEM RERUN ALL NEXT SUMMER!"

SIR, THIS IS THE STATE DEPARTMENT... WE HAVE A CRISIS BREWING IN...
TAKE TWO ASPIRIN AND CALL ME IN THE MORNING!
HE EXPANDED HIS HEALTH-CARE PLAN TO COVER FOREIGN AFFAIRS!
PRESIDENT CLINTON
STAYSKAL 93 TAMPA TRIBUNE

NAT'L HEALTH CARE SERVICE CLINIC # 14,620-3AK
PATIENTS: IF YOUR NUMBER IS BETWEEN B56130236 AND L93042615, SEE DOCTORS MD305211 THROUGH MD799026 FOR APPOINTMENT ASSIGNMENTS. IF THE LAST 2 DIGITS OF YOUR NUMBER EQUAL 9, CALL THE 1-900-202-CLINTON VOICEMAIL HOT LINE. YOUR CALL WILL BE RETURNED WITHIN 64 HOURS. ALL OTHER PATIENTS WITH NUMBERS NOT MENTIONED ABOVE PLEASE BE PATIENT.
STAYSKAL 93 TAMPA TRIBUNE

"THE FIRST DETECTOR IS FOR GUNS AND KNIVES... THE SECOND ONE CHECKS FOR RELIGIOUS MATERIAL!"

STAYSKAL
93 TAMPA
TRIBUNE
JUVENILE
CRIME
WORSENS

DON'T WORRY, WE'LL MAKE SURE YOU PULL THROUGH... WE CAN'T LOSE SOMEBODY IN THE HIGHEST TAX BRACKET NOW CAN WE?
GOV'T
HEALTH CARE
STAYSKAL
93 TAMPA
TRIBUNE

YOU ACTUALLY BELIEVE CLINTON'S HEALTH-CARE PLAN WILL RESULT IN JOB GAINS?
ABSOLUTELY... JUST THINK OF ALL THE PEOPLE IT'LL TAKE TO STRAIGHTEN OUT THE MESS IT'LL GET US INTO!
ECONOMIST
ECONOMIST
STAYSKAL 93 TAMPA TRIBUNE

STAYSKAL 93 TAMPA TRIBUNE
THE PRESSURE'S WAY DOWN... HARDLY ANY WATER IS COMING IN!
HEY... DON'T KNOCK IT!
NEWS: U.S. STANDARDS FOR SAFE TAP WATER SLIPPING, SAYS STUDY

PERSONALLY, I THINK WE NEED A PRESIDENT WHO'S OLDER!
YOU'RE RIGHT... BUT DO YOU THINK GEORGE BURNS WOULD RUN?
DOLE'S AGE A FACTOR?
STAYSKAL 95 TAMPA TRIBUNE

STAYSKAL 93 TAMPA TRIBUNE
CRITICS OF HUMAN CLONING SAY THE RESULTS COULD BE 'CHILLING'!
WHAT COULD THEY MEAN?
SEARCH ME!
I'LL ASK THE HILLARYS AND SEE IF THEY KNOW!
PRESIDENTS OF THE UNITED STATES

"THIS IS AN UPDATED VERSION OF 'ROMEO AND JULIET'... HE GETS HIT WITH A SEXUAL HARASSMENT SUIT!"

NAT'L HUMANITIES ENDOWMENT SPENDS $870,500 TO ENGAGE PEOPLE IN TALKING ABOUT WHAT IT MEANS TO BE AN AMERICAN
AS AN AMERICAN I DON'T LIKE TAXES USED LIKE THIS, OR FOR THE ARTS ENDOWMENT, OR FOR...
YOU'RE OUT OF ORDER, SIR!
EXIT
PUBLIC FORUM
SPONSORED BY YOUR NAT'L GOV'T
STAYSKAL 95 TAMPA TRIBUNE

PSSSST... CALVIN KLEIN JEANS COMMERCIALS?
STAYSKAL 95 TAMPA TRIBUNE

PRESIDENT CLINTON SAYS HE IS CONSIDERING A PLAN TO LICENSE GUN OWNERS TO SLOW SURGE OF VIOLENT CRIMES
MAY I SEE YOUR LICENSE, PLEASE?
STAYSKAL 93 TAMPA TRIBUNE

HILLARY INVESTED $1000; MADE $100,000 IN COMMODITIES TRADING
THAT'S RIGHT... I'VE GOT $52.70 AND I WANT TO PUT IT IN PORK BELLIES OR SOWS' EARS OR WHATEVER IT WAS HILLARY GOT INTO!
COOKIE JAR
STAYSKAL 94 TAMPA TRIBUNE

STAYSKAL '94 TAMPA TRIBUNE
SCIENTISTS AND ENTREPRENEURS REVIVE SEARCH FOR INTELLIGENT LIFE IN THE UNIVERSE.
MIGHT AS WELL... FINDING ANY DOWN HERE IS A LOST CAUSE!

HOW TO PROVE SWIMSUITS HAVE NOTHING TO DO WITH THE MISS AMERICA SWIMSUIT COMPETITION
AND NOW, WHAT YOU'VE BEEN WAITING FOR...
1.
2.
3.
4.
5.
6.
STAYSKAL '95 TAMPA TRIBUNE

"I'M GLAD CLINTON WAS TOUGH ON CRIME IN HIS STATE OF THE UNION SPEECH ... MAYBE WE'LL SEE SOME ACTION NOW!"

CLINTON HEALTH CARE ADMINISTRATION BUILDING
YOU ARE HERE
1 2 3 4 5 10
SCALE IN MILES
STAYSKAL '94 TAMPA TRIBUNE

CLINTON STAKES CLAIM TO GOP TURF IN RECENT SPEECHES
NOW TO FIND OUT WHAT I'VE BEEN TALKING ABOUT...
LET'S SEE... 'CRIME'... 'WELFARE REFORM'... 'PERSONAL RESPONSIBILITY'... 'FAMILY VALUES'...
DICTIONARY
STAYSKAL '94 TAMPA TRIBUNE

IF PRESENT TRENDS CONTINUE, TODAY'S NEWBORNS WILL PAY MORE THAN HALF OF WHAT THEY'LL EARN IN TAXES
NURSERY
MATERNITY
IRS
STAYSKAL
94 TAMPA TRIBUNE

PTA MEETING
WHEN I CAME HERE AS A KID THAT'S WHERE THE TEN COMMANDMENTS USED TO HANG!
PRESIDENT CLINTON'S RELIGIOUS ACTIVITIES GUIDELINES
JANE
BILLY S.
JOE P.
STAYSKAL
95 TAMPA TRIBUNE